Flying High

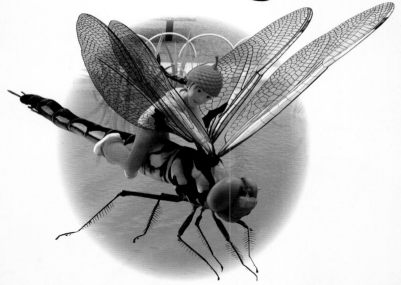

Gina Nuttall
Illustrated by Jon Stuart

OXFORD

In this story

Cat

Tiger

micro-copter

dragonfly

Cat and Tiger were outside the den.
They pushed the buttons ...

Tiger wanted to fly.
He took Max's micro-copter.
He put the straps on.

"I wish we had two micro-copters,"
said Cat.

Just then they saw a dark shadow.
They looked up and saw a big insect.

It landed nearby.
"Look!" said Cat. "It is a dragonfly."
Cat had an idea …

She got on the dragonfly's back.
"We could have a race," she said.
"Race you across the pond!"

"Cool!" said Tiger. "Let's go!"
Off he flew in the micro-copter.
Then Cat and the dragonfly took off.

Cat and Tiger raced out across the pond.

Tiger zoomed up and down
in the micro-copter.
Cat zig-zagged on the dragonfly.
She was in the lead.

Just then Cat saw a bee.
"Oh, no!" she cried.
The dragonfly zig-zagged away from
the bee. Cat held on.

Then Tiger saw a bird.
He zoomed up out of the way.
"Oh, no!" cried Cat.
"Birds eat dragonflies."

The dragonfly zig-zagged away from the bird. It flew down and down. It landed on the other side of the pond. Cat jumped off its back.

Tiger landed nearby.

"Are you OK, Cat?" said Tiger.

"Yes," said Cat. "I won!"

"Oh, yeah," said Tiger. "Race you back?"

Dragonfly facts

- Dragonflies can fly forwards, backwards and sideways.
- Dragonflies are the fastest flying insects in the world.
- Dragonflies have four wings.

big eyes

four wings

long body